Computers are makin
horseracing, with a wid
help crack the game. In his Computer Corner column in ODDS ON magazine, Robin Lloyd, journalist and racing enthusiast for 45 years, has put dozens of programs under starter's orders.

You don't have to be computer literate or even a racefan to run most of these user-friendly offerings. Here Robin Lloyd looks afresh at these programs and gives you the form and SP.

Plus there's a new section giving advice on suitable hardware, and a short article by Nick Mordin detailing developments on the Internet.

If you are planning to buy racing software, check out the field!

——— ❖ ———

Other books currently published by Aesculus Press

Against the Crowd by Alan Potts
The Winning Look by Nick Mordin
Betting for a Living by Nick Mordin
One Hundred Hints for Better Betting by Mark Coton
Counterpain by Trixie
Coups & Cons by Graham Sharpe

For further details of the above titles please write to:

Aesculus Press
PO Box 10
Oswestry
Shropshire
SY10 7QR

or telephone: 01691 791426

COMPUTING Winners

A Guide to Racing Computer Programs

Robin Lloyd

Aesculus Press

First Published 1995
by Aesculus Press,
P.O.Box 10, Oswestry,
Shropshire SY10 7QR.

Typeset by Aesculus Press using MICROSOFT WORD
Output on a Hewlett Packard HP Laserjet 4.

Printed and bound in Great Britain by Images, Malvern Wells

1-871093-97-X

Contents

Saddle up 7

Going behind 11

Key to the ratings 13

In the stalls 14
A-Z of racing computer programs

A share of the action 52

Winners' enclosure 54

Scratched? Or gone to stud? 56

Weighing in 58

Everything you ever wanted to know about horseracing - via your modem *by Nick Mordin* 60

A warning and disclaimer

You should gamble only with money you can comfortably afford to lose. The write-ups and ratings are presented as guidance only, not as praise or condemnation of any product. No claim or guarantee is made or implied. Neither the publisher nor the author takes responsibility for losses arising from the adoption or non-adoption of the advice or information.

Saddle up

If you have never used a computer but are tempted to buy one even, if only to run gambling programs, a brief description of what is required may help you harness your facts.

I hope you will find encouragement here, especially when I tell you I am almost a novice in this technology.

Computer buffs may skip this chapter - or stick around for horse laughs at my expense!

My first computer, a Spectrum 48, was a 1985 retirement gift from colleagues. The 'Speccy' is acquiring cult status and secondhand sets are still being advertised. However, don't look for a Spectrum or any other of that ilk if you want to take your compupunting seriously.

The first software I bought, also in 1985, cost just over £100. It comprised Martin Thompson's Brimardon suite of several horseracing programs with print-outs of them. These programs showed up well financially and the Spectrum displayed them on my television screen.

After much fine-tuning down the years, the Brimardon programs are still doing well: rated five-star, they are now made mainly for the personal computer.

Today's PCs, which are IBMs or IBM compatibles, are in a completely different class from the Spectrum - Ferraris compared to bubble cars. Some very old model secondhand PCs (Metros, to continue the analogy) may be bought for little more than what a Spectrum costs.

Look for advertisements in your local paper or in magazines such as the weekly micromart for old PCs like the Amstrad 1512 (the technology breakthrough model of the mid-eighties) and 1640.

You may also put in Wanted ads free in most of these publications.

An acquaintance is quite happy with an Amstrad 1512 that he bought for £50. It has a 20Mb hard disk and runs DOS versions of Brimardon, Boxform and my Bet Better on the two floppy drives.

A fair price for an Amstrad 1640 is about £70-80.

If you buy any such a model with a hard disk, copy your programs onto it as the floppy diskettes on which almost all programs are sold can easily be damaged. You should, of course, first make a back-up copy of the program. And make sure the machine is loaded with DOS.

The monitors are in mono (black and white).

Amstrads and other makes of the same era are being offloaded by enthusiasts clamouring for the latest state-of-the-art machines now that prices have tumbled.

The big differences between computers like the Spectrum and PCs is in the vastly superior microchip power, allowing huge memory storage and performing functions with great speed. To begin with, perhaps all you need to know about memory, measured in Megabytes and Kilobytes, is that the more you have the merrier. Today's standard PCs have hard disks of around 200Mb. Memory is also needed to run the computer's system.

Computer jargon is rampant with acronyms and you will hear words like RAM and ROM bandied about for both functions: plenty of time later to get to grips with Random Access Memory and Read Only Memory. For the time being bear in mind that if you want to run ever more hefty racing and other programs you should go for at least a 200Mb hard disk and 4Mb RAM.

Since 1988, I have used PCs, Apple Macintoshes and other machines while working part-time for different publications. Then I bought my first PC from bankrupt stock late in 1991. A 386SX x 25mhz model (386 Central Processor Unit chip, 25 megahertz speed), it had a 42Mb hard drive and two floppies, a 5.25 inch and a 3.5 inch.

Few new machines now incorporate a 5.25 inch drive and very few new programs accommodate this dying size.

I paid around £1,000 for my Datek/AST hybrid and its specifications were pretty nearly top of the range.

Twice since then I have had to upgrade to keep pace with additions to my hard disk of some of the weightier programs I review for ODDS ON. The 42Mb was replaced in April 1994 by a 252Mb disk costing some £210. At the same time, for around a further £250, I had the 386 CPU chip replaced by a 486 chip and the Megahertz rating upped from 25 to 33 to speed up the computer.

In September 1995, I added a 550Mb drive (£120) to the 252Mb disk. The other memory was increased from 2Mb to 4Mb and then to 8Mb, the necessary SIMMS chips for these operations costing £100 and £120 respectively. All these parts went into the computer's motherboard, where there are also slots for video and other cards and their upgrades.

Memory-hungry programs include RacingSystemBuilder (44Mb for Professional edition) and Computer Form Book, Computer Raceform, Computer Timeform and Solidus (all from 30Mb+ and growing with the regular data updates).

Looking further ahead, and to spoil myself, I have also bought a multimedia CD-ROM drive which takes floppies holding the equivalent of a million pages of text.

It also plays music, shows pictures and so on.

The £350 package included several good CD-ROMs. But multi-media outfits are by no means essential.

The latest Pentium chip, with superfast processing speeds, may be next on my acquisition list.

I mention models and components to illustrate how dramatically prices have fallen.

At the time of writing, the technician who privately upgraded my computer can put together a 486DX x 33Mhz computer with 500Mb hard drive and 4Mb RAM, plus a 3.5 high density floppy drive, keyboard, mouse and other peripherals for around £580.

The mouse is a hand-held device on a roller ball that enables you when in Windows and some DOS programs to point to the spot where you want to make alterations and perform other tasks.

Almost all computers are now sold with a monitor (screen), mouse, probably an integrated software package comprising wordprocessor, spreadsheet and database programs, and two operating systems, Microsoft DOS - 'Disk Operating System' - and Microsoft Windows 3.1 or the latest Windows 95.

Professional friends advise waiting for the second version of Windows 95 for any faults to be corrected. Moreover, some programs taking Windows 3.1 will not run on Windows 95, so inquire before you buy.

The DOS commands need to be learned, but you won't need many of them to get you moving in Windows. In this user-friendly interface you see virtually what you get. Almost all new racing programs and revised older ones are in Windows.

For the computer tyro, Windows allied to user-friendly racing software is a godsend. Loading is simple and operating the programs generally involves nothing more difficult than supplying the data requested from racing papers.

If you have taken more than a few cigars from the bookie and are buying new it is advisable to aim for at least a 486DX x 66 computer with 450Mb hard drive and 8Mb RAM to keep pace with the ever more demanding Windows software. For less, and at a pinch, you may just get away with a 386SX x 25 with 100Mb disk and 2 to 4Mb RAM for some programs.

Most monitors now take colour. Resolution, measured in pixels, conforms to the VGA (Video Graphics Array) system introduced by IBM in 1987. Top of the range: SVGA (Super VGA).

Printers come in three forms: laser, dot matrix and ink/bubble jet. In terms of price, running costs and quality, lasers head the list, followed by ink/bubble jets and then dot matrixes. The last named are probably most popular with home users, being earlier on the scene than the jets, which are overtaking them in sales due to better quality results.

With laser printer prices slashed, more of these machines are finding their way into private houses.

Should you be offered a daisywheel printer summon up a pitying look and pretend to be deaf - it's antiquated toy stuff, though sentimental diehards will differ.

As yet, and unlike the Spectrum, daisywheels are not cult objects.

I myself have made do quite adequately for four years with a portable Starjet SJ-48 for black and white printing. I have changed to an Epson Stylus Color Jet to enhance publicity printing for my business.

The Starjet cost around £230 but its equivalents may now be bought for far less. The Epson has set me back some £390.

You may also wonder about modems (modulator/demodulator). These devices transmit data on phone lines. They can fit inside the computer on a plug-in card or be a standalone plugged into a serial port. I am told the former are cheaper and more popular.

The Kingsdown company, who make life easier for users of such heavy input programs as Pro-Punter, Brimardon and Betting Manager, transmit up-to-date race data down these lines.

The Kingsdown service proved excellent when I tested it with Betting Manager's Speedmaster and I feel sure it is also proving a godsend to the other programs mentioned.

A modem with a high speed (baud) rate will keep the phone bill down.

If you are deep into the dreaded losing run forget about such an enhancement, and even forego a printer for now: your racing program forecasts may be copied in pen and paper off the screen.

And don't, if you are tempted, buy one of those excellent but expensive Apple Macintoshes to run racing software. I have heard of only one such piece of software for the Macs.

Besides the desktop computers I have been describing there are laptop portables on which, depending on the specifications, you can run most if not all the desktop programs.

The pocket size Psions are not in this league, having a much more limited capacity and fewer and poorer racing programs. Whether Psions are a worthwhile asset on racecourse or in betshop to take in the latest odds is up to individuals to decide.

But remember, with the latest technology desktop users can, for an ever diminishing price, tap into Teletext odds available in the ring and bet through modems to such layers as Betpoint.

And watch the races live on their monitors!

Finally, buy the best machine you can afford. The rest of the family will also soon want to use it for at least one of the following: education, games, business, the Internet . . .

Going behind

'Are there really any winning programs? And if there are, why should anyone want to put them on the market?'

These reasonable questions are often asked. I would reply that several programs listed in this book have proved they can win, though there is no guarantee that they will forever.

Why put them on the market?

One answer is obviously 'Money'. Another, perhaps, is pride, ego, call it what you will, for which the enjoyment diminishes the longer the method is kept secret. Other reasons could include the desire to help fellow punters or to get back at the bookmakers. One successful programmer says he is getting even with the bookmakers after being banned by some 30 or so of them.

I myself, having survived heart attacks that cut short my full-time journalistic career, decided to go public with my Bet Better program after being told I had a leaky aortic valve - and cancer!

I decided to encapsulate in a simple, user-friendly disk decades of moderate success with various methods.

Thus, I thought, I might be able to help fellow punters, beginners and (dare I say it?) pros, in the sport that has given me much pleasure for decades.

And thus, purchasers in turn would help me eke out an abbreviated pension but more importantly provide a small source of income for my widow.

After all, in addition to dreaded ailments, I had reached that Biblical benchmark age beyond which was to live on borrowed time . . .

Gloom and doom, I am glad to say, vanished faster than it took Dancing Brave to win the Arc when the Great Steward in the Sky decreed that the Big C prognosis was groundless.

So there you have one punter's motive for marketing his product.

As for profit from programs, surely Artificial Intelligence can one day do for horserace forecasting what it has done to Chess, where the computer is beating Grand Masters.

Like the alchemists of old who sought the mythical Philosopher's Stone to turn base metal into gold, today's programmers crunch numbers to try to turn horses into fortunes. Many of these efforts can be a great help to the punter.

So, congratulations! You now hold probably the only book of its kind in the world that has brought such a collection of reviews together. May the money you paid for it be amply repaid.

Whether or not you are new to computing, or even to horseracing, you could be entering an Aladdin's cave. Even the humblest computer could be your Abracadabra to move aside the rock. The jewels are the software gleaming with the promise of opulence.

The Personal Computer was born only in the early eighties. Since then there have been breathtaking breakthroughs in machines and user-friendly software. And prices have tumbled.

The programs reviewed here all run on the PC, most needing modest machines, some more powerful ones; many can also operate on the less powerful micros, the Amigas and Ataris.

There is also, I believe, a Shareware program costing only £1 that will allow the running of some PC software on the Atari ST/STE.

Heavyweight programs costing around £500 carry the results of a season or two and, as mentioned in the previous chapter, need a machine with plenty of memory all round. These programs are usually kept up to the mark with a weekly or even a daily update of results.

But most of the software is standalone, costing from a mere £3 or so to £150 for a one-off payment. They leave more of the inputting to the punter. Many run on DOS, though programmers are turning increasingly to Windows.

In varying degrees all the programs give the punter a good chance of winning. They exclude guesswork and hunches. They pack much more power to analyse quickly the most complex methods.

A good track record over several years, ten preferably, is adequate proof of the potency of a system - or racing software. At least two programs have stood this test of time. Several newer ones show signs of going the distance.

However, it cannot be stressed strongly enough that most of the findings here are from a very small sampling. Like the opinions and ratings, they should be treated cautiously. They represent one person's opinions and are meant primarily as a guide, not as tablets of stone from on high.

They also try to avoid being dazzled by short-term-itis, a malady found where programmers' proofed selections are published in a table of merit for a few months of Saturdays.

A program may top the list for a few months while hitting a purple patch. Meanwhile, at the bottom of the list could be a program suffering a long succession of losers but which is, nevertheless, more successful software in the long term.

This leads me to the matter of choice, where temperament plays a big part. How many will stick with a profitable program when it is suffering one of its frequent and frighteningly long losing runs? Will it be easier on the nerves and heart to go for a less successful offering that has a higher hit-rate?

This book should hopefully help the punter pick something suitable to individual taste. But remember, though the ratings are generally based on results they express an individual human view and the same individual's temperament.

And so it must be, until or unless the computer takes over completely with a thoroughly clinical assessment.

Key to the ratings

★★★★★	Outstanding
★★★★	Above Average
★★★	Average
★★	Below Average
★	Poor

In the stalls

So here are the runners. Always check for the latest prices (special offers, etc) before the off.

Remember, too, that some stables have double entries, pacemakers in the form of Shareware versions or demos, free or for very little cash.

And bear in mind that some Windows programs will not run on Windows 95.

It is wise always to check to ensure you are fully abreast of exactly what is on offer - the latest form, if you like.

AMP: ARTUS MANAGER PLUS v5.0

Price: £79

Artus Software, P O Box 4430, London SW3 3XD. Phone: 0181 678 0607.

Company profile:

Small part-time business. Established 1987 in France, 1992 in the UK. Besides having overseas markets they also sell gambling books.

Technical details:

PCs 286 or higher. DOS 3.1 or later. 3Mb hard disk space. Will not run from floppy disk.

Software Type:

Winner-finding on the Architect Method, a procedure to find betting combinations of all types (Tricasts, etc).

Overview:

A novel French entrant.

Ease of Use:

Hard to get into at first but big efforts have been made and language problems eased. Time taken to get into new approach could benefit the adventurous.

Documentation:

Written:

Suggestions followed for step-by-step instructions.

On Screen:

Review disks showed some instructions in French but these were easy enough to unravel.

Technical support:

Lifetime telephone support offered.

Visual:

Colour and mono. Not spectacular.

Range and versatility: ★★

Little beyond a novel approach to winning on multi-bets.

Value For Money: 

Despite low ratings for other features, a program likely to please many, particularly the go-for-broke gambler.

FOR:

Gallic dash most pleasing. Perseverence could result in big returns. Discounts for updates.

AGAINST:

New approach takes some getting used to.

VERDICT:

Quirky but refreshingly original. May not appeal to the followers of tried and trusted approaches, but for the adventurous it's French without fears.

The following program, by the author of this book, has been independently reviewed by long-time programmer and businessman Steve Marriott.

BET BETTER v3.1

Price: £48.50

Cheques to Robin Lloyd, c/o Money Flow Promotions, 19 St Andrew Street, Tiverton, Devon EX16 6PH. Phone: Orders & technical support 0118 425 4103; author's personal number for betting advice 0117 940 2478.

Company profile:

Programmer David Lacy-Hulbert, Joint Venture software writer since 1985. Subjects covered include Languages tuition, Agriculture, writers' plot blocks, horseracing, odds calculator. Author Robin Lloyd, decades into racing. Software reviewer, principally of gambling software, since 1985.

Technical details:

DOS version runs on PCs with 512K and DOS 3.1 or higher. It may be run from the floppy or installed to hard disk. Windows 3.1 version requires 2Mb RAM; 386PCs (at least), 486 recommended, with 2.6Mb hard disk space.

Software Type:

Out and out winner-finding for both the Flat and National Hunt. In Windows or DOS (buyer must stipulate which wanted).

Overview:

Concentrates on six key factors: prize money, strike-rate, class, speed, recent form and suitability to course and distance. Going and draw left to punter to elucidate from the Racing Post.

Ease of Use: ★★★★★

Installation could be easier, but worth the wait. Simple to use but it would be nice to see all the horses in grid.

Documentation: ★★★★★

Written:

Instructions on the disk.

On Screen:

Help screens outstanding - based on the Racing Post.

Technical support:

Free support and advice available by phone.

Visual: ★★★★

Easy on the eye - important when data is being input very early in the morning.

Range and versatility: ★★

Straightforward winner-finder.

Value For Money: ★★★★★

Yes!

FOR:

Help screens and documentation reflect the author's background as a journalist.

AGAINST:

Non-standard Windows intake and drop-off of results on races in the low value group.

VERDICT:

An easy to use, well documented program. A valuable addition to anyone's horseracing software.

BETTING MANAGER v2.0 Pro

Price: £79

3 Pemdevon Road, Croydon, Surrey CRO 3QQ. Phone: 0181 689 8875.

Company profile:

The author has riding and first hand racing experience at the sharp end. His father trained Flat and National Hunt horses for 18 years. Full-time expanding business.

Technical details:

Runs on IBM compatible PCs, 386 processor or higher. Windows. Minimum

2Mb RAM, 6Mb free hard disk space. VGA graphics or SVGA (with VGA graphics). Upgrades free for first 12 months on return of original disks and £2 p&p. After 12 months, upgrades priced according to major/minor - £10 to £30.

Software Type:
Winner-finding for Flat and National Hunt.

Overview:
Instantaneous multi-bet calculations. Average selection method. Bursting with utilities.

Ease of Use: ★★★
Fairly easy. Early loading problems overcome.

Documentation: ★★★
Written:
24-page booklet.

On Screen:
Overview demo and tutorial. Windows help.

Technical support:
Help line to 9pm. Advice on program operation and general aspects of betting. Custom-built hardware supplied with all software installed. Full technical support. Callers welcome.

Visual: ★★★★
The betting slip graphics are stunning. Colour coding makes everything simple. The most colourful of all the programs reviewed.

Range and versatility:

Good staking system through the AutoStaker. Combinations perms (with a breakdown of the combinations) are quickly sorted out. Keeps betting bank(s) records (fully auto - no inputs). Calculates returns on all popular bets. Course descriptions and maps. Notebook. Racing Calendar and Diary, plus other betting utilities.

Value For Money:

Yes, now the price has come down from £149.

FOR:
Superb graphics. Plenty of utilities. Exciting potential for big wins.

AGAINST:
Basic rating system.

VERDICT:
Worth keeping on the computer for its accurate, lightning-fast calculation of complicated multi-bets. Slay a Goliath on a fun day?

BETTING MANAGER SPEEDMASTER

Price: £159

Address as for Betting Manager.

Company profile:

As for Betting Manager.

Technical details:

Runs on IBM compatible PCs, 386 processor or higher (486 recommended). Windows 3.1, 3.11 and Windows 95. Minimum 4Mb RAM. 10Mb disk space with data.

Software Type:

Winner-finding for Flat and National Hunt.

Overview:

Speed the essence, coupled with form. The program generates its own speed figures using real times of previous races (source Raceform Update).

Ease of Use:

Laborious manually. But ratings in seconds claimed if downloading data and daily race cards from Kingsdown Racing's bulletin board.

Documentation: ★★★

Written:

38-page tutorial booklet.

On Screen:

Windows help and program message prompts.

Visual: ★★★★

As with Betting Master it is visually colourful and clear.

Technical support:

Help line till 9pm. Advice on program operation and general aspects of betting. Full technical support. Callers welcome.

Range and versatility:

Extensive, like its Betting Manager stablemate. Keeps betting banks and manages staking, course descriptions and maps. Notebook, racing calendar and diary plus many other betting utilities. Horses to Follow option automatically checked against day's runners.

Value For Money:

Check for promotional discounts. Update disk and modem service add to costs.

FOR:

Easy to use with race cards. Scientific speed approach. Results encouraging. Superb graphics. Pampered with betting utilities. Minor upgrades free from

Kingsdown bulletin board. Upgraded disks available if requested.

AGAINST:

Time-consuming if input is manual. Needs a modem to make best use of racing facilities.

VERDICT:

Kingsdown Racing boosts the speed in Speedmaster. A fine all round program that has overcome early bugs.

BOXFORM TOOLKIT

Price: £39.95

Boxform, 65 Allans Meadow, Neston, South Wirral L64 9SQ.
Phone: 0151 336 2668.

***Racing Boxform** (£21.95 if bought on its own) comes into the ring backed up by several other programs, all comprising the Racing Toolkit.*

The Toolkit includes Handicap Winner, Horse Sort and Personal Racing Record, Punter's Partner and Punter's Pal, a lovely offering that works out time and other ratings with weight-for-age reckoning where necessary. These programs may be bought separately.

Company profile:

Small full-time business. Established 1985. Lots of other sporting software, mainly football orientated.

Technical details:

PCs. Hard disk unnecessary. Versions of most programs available for all PCW and old 8-bit machines.

Software Type:

Winner-finding from several angles, with other programs to tie up the loose bits.

Overview:

Bursting with features.

Ease of Use: 

Will make the beginner feel like an expert. But two programs on one disk leads to confusion.

Documentation: 

Written:

Copious information on scrolling sheets. Not so good but keeps the price down. Booklet planned.

On Screen:

General.

Technical support:
By phone or letter at any time.

Visual: ★
Looks old-fashioned in black and white; but remember, some of the old movies are considered among the best.

Range and versatility: ★★★★
Considerable. Three winner-finding programs, plus personal records and a bets calculator.

Value For Money: ★★★
A lot for comparatively little.

FOR:
The add your own factors facility and Best Bet of the Day feature in Racing Boxform, the power of Handicap Winner and the simplicity of the Punter's Pal rating method.

AGAINST:
Dull look. Folded sheet documentation. No hint that the two main programs are on one disk. Omission of Best Bet of the Day from Handicap Winner.

VERDICT:
Straightforward offerings with plenty of punching power.

BOXFORM WINDOW ON RACING

Price: £29.95
Address as for Boxform Toolkit.

NB. *Boxform also produce* **Window on Football Betting** *which costs £29.95.*

Company profile:
As for Boxform Toolkit.

Technical details:
For Windows.

Software Type:
Form analysis.

Overview:
Best results from Racing Post but daily newspapers may be used instead. Helpful for beginners trying to figure out a racecard and racing terms.

Ease of Use: ★★★★
Quick inputting from Racing Post data, particularly Postdata. Well laid out.

Documentation:

Written:
Six laser-printed sheets of instructions, observations and advice. Lacks instruction for last item of input for each horse in Race Analysis.

On Screen:
General.

Technical support:
By phone or letter at any time.

Visual: ★★★
Big improvement in looks over mono Boxform. Attractive screens.

Range and versatility:

Good. Besides the winner-finder, there are graphs and a ready reckoner for single and multiple bets. Fine colour-coded racecourse details.

Value For Money:

Competitively priced for a lot offered.

FOR:
Quick and easy inputting. A little for a lot. Fairly accurate.

AGAINST:
Better if program stood by its own rating rather than incorporate another's overall figure (Postmark's, from the Racing Post). Some possible duplication of form assessment could corrupt the finding. A widely used rating also cuts value for money.

VERDICT:
A likeable program reasonably priced.

BRED FAST-TRACK

Price: £45

Bred, 19 Cherry Way, Upper Halliford, Shepperton, Middlesex TW17 8QQ. Phone: 01932 883214.

Company profile:
Small publisher, established 1992. Program developed August 1994.

Technical details:
386+PCs. Windows 3.1. Allow for 2-3Mb on hard disk and at least 2Mb RAM.

Software Type:
Winner finding through bloodlines, for Flat.

Overview:
A novel, specialised approach to winner-finding. Could be the clincher when assessing selections by other programs.

Ease of Use: ★★★

Different - and difficult to begin with.

Documentation: ★★

Written:

Two-page tutorial.

On Screen:

Comprehensive.

Technical support:

None officially given, because none needed. However, problems or points are personally attended to, although this is strictly on the basis of wanting to provide customer care, not as a consumer right.

Visual: ★★

Colour.

Range and versatility: ★★

Mainly limited to breeding, but also has an informative menu on Courses.

Value For Money: ★★

Yes, as it covers a neglected aspect of winner-finding. But not favoured as a stand-alone.

FOR:

Outstanding attempt to deal in detail with a generally neglected aspect.

AGAINST:

Gaps in the sires listed precludes predicting some winners in valuable races. Loading problems. Get the all clear before you buy.

VERDICT:

A valuable piece in the jigsaw but not a complete solution in itself.

BRIMARDON FORMULA PLUS

Price: £55 (Flat and National Hunt versions)

Brimardon Computer Racing Service, 75 Cockerton Green, Darlington DL3 9EG. Phone: 01325 288483.

Company profile:

Established 1984. Small part-time business selling only horseracing software directly to customers. Software written by people with racing backgrounds and much racing knowledge.

Technical details:

PCs 286 or later, earlier versions available for Commodore 68/128, Amstrad CPC, Amstrad PCW (3 and 3.5 inch), Amiga and Atari ST (Price £40).

Software Type:
Winner-finding for Flat and National Hunt. Programs regularly updated and improved. Small charges for annual updates.

Overview:
A pioneer sticking to the milestones of success. Increased number of features with latest version. Meticulous in what it does.

Ease of Use: ★★★
Vast improvement on earlier versions. Optional database cuts data entry time to the minimum. Weekly updates either by modem or disk from Kingsdown Racing (01920 830278, £5 a week with discounts). Race details can be saved to file.

Documentation: ★★★
Written:
Comprehensive 12-15 page booklets with all software. Full instructions and advice provided on best races to concentrate on and other useful information.

On Screen:
Full on-screen help for all sections of the program.

Technical support:
Personal attention given to all inquiries, either written or on the phone. Feedback from customers welcomed as changes have been made in the light of customer suggestions. Personal callers welcome.

Visual: ★★★
Colour and mono.

Range and versatility: ★★★★
Considerable. A vast difference from very earlier pioneering versions. Full race analysis ratings, odds, value for money advice, Horse File facility (blinkers, trainer's intentions etc).

Value For Money: ★★★★★
Small price to pay for success.

FOR:
Good level-stake profit every Flat and NH season since 1985 - including a winner at 100-1! High strike-rate from better class races. Helpful Value Bet tips and, to be ignored at one's peril, the Veto message. Emphasis on Class.

AGAINST:
Data entry disks add to cost, otherwise it's still a hard slog acquiring input data from racing papers.

VERDICT:
What beats year upon year of success?

COMBAYES

Price: £39.95

DFL Software Company, 13 Holly Road, Northampton NN1 4QL. Phone: 01604 24744.

Company profile:

Small software house. Established 1990 but collating PC software since 1985. It sells a huge variety of gambling programs, including its own Compunter for Football and much shareware. The founder/programmer is a former accountant and licensed bookmaker. He started and runs the international Gambling Software Users Club, where boffins abound.

Technical details:

PCs, DOS 2.1 or later. Hard disk not required but advisable.

Software Type:

Winner-finder for National Hunt and Flat - separate versions.

Overview:

Simple and quick to use - less than two minutes inputting per race. It was evolved from 18 spreadsheets with nearly 2Mb of formulae on each. Each-way betting advised.

Ease of Use: ★★★★★

Could not be easier.

Documentation: ★★

Written:

Newsletter type.

On Screen:

Help on jockeys, trainers etc.

Technical support:

Encourages customer contact.

Visual: ★★

Colour and mono.

Range and versatility: ★★

No bells and whistles, just quick, straight forecasting.

Value For Money:

Competitively priced. A lot of power for little effort.

FOR:

As quick as they come. A boon for the busy punter. A level-stake profit each year.

AGAINST:

Seems to do well for half a season only.

VERDICT:

A good one to have in your armoury. Can it ever emulate its evolutionary year, 1992/93, when from 119 selections and a tenner it made a paper profit of £3,392,140.40 tax paid!

COMPUNTER

Price: £39.95

Address and phone number as for Combayes.

Company profile:

See Combayes.

Technical details:

See Combayes.

Software Type:

Value betting winner-finder for Flat and National Hunt. A separate DFL program, Racelect (£9.95), evaluates the day's races into the order in which Compunter has historically been most successful and is essentially for use with Compunter, though not a vital part of it.

Overview:

Not for the fainthearted, can have long losing runs. Value for money is the aim. Published results are from Saturdays and Bank Holidays only. A good staking plan.

Ease of Use: ★★★

User-friendly, but watch out for possible ambiguity in jockey/trainer initials when inputting. Three modes: the quickie is very quick and its findings virtually the same as those of the other two.

Documentation: ★★

Written:

See Combayes.

On Screen:

See Combayes.

Technical support:

See Combayes.

Visual: ★★

See Combayes.

Range and versatility: ★★

More innards and 'outards' than the sister program, Combayes, but no real frills.

Value For Money: 

Massive winning potential, a yardstick against which all the others may be compared.

FOR:

The know-how of a former bookmaker and accountant behind years of profits. A good staking system.

AGAINST:

Dips - and sometimes starts - horrifically. Can you bear to wager a grand or two after a long losing run? The Going not considered.

VERDICT:

With perseverence, one of the best money-makers.

COMPUTER FORM BOOK

Price: Check. Prices fall as season progresses.
Trial subscriptions: Four weeks, £39; Ten weeks, £99.
Continuation subscriptions: Four weeks, £38.90; ten weeks, £95.60.

OEM Computer Systems, Rugby Micro Centre, 1 Regent Street, Rugby, Warwickshire, CV21 2PE. Phone: 01788 570522.

Company profile:

Established at the same address in 1981. Software/Hardware development and solutions to industry. Leisure software with the Computer Form Book since 1990.

Technical details:

PCs. Separate DOS and Windows programs. Separate Flat and National Hunt programs. Allow for 640K RAM and 30Mb free hard disk space and for 2Mb per data update disk twice weekly. CFB for Windows requires minimum 386 processor.

Software Type:

Full-blown form book on your own computer, listing full race details of every run of every horse in every race in the UK. Also includes major races from abroad. Masses of statistical analysis by Horse, Trainer, Jockey etc plus a highly successful Form and Speed ratings service. Pre-season discounts to past subscribers for full-season subscriptions.

Overview:

Almost a complete service, as one would expect for the price.

Ease of Use: 

Very easy to jockey through multitudes of features and statistics, particularly in the Windows version.

Documentation: 

Written:
Bound manuals with clear instructions.

On Screen:
Guidance.

Technical support:
Full technical support from an expert team Monday to Friday 9am to 5.30pm.

Visual: ★★★
Colour DOS and Windows, and mono (DOS only).

Range and versatility:

To the farthest known corners of computer forecasting, swapping horses with the greatest of ease. INSIGHT feature with screenfuls of analysis, THE MARKET homes in on true odds.

Value For Money:

A lot of money, a lot of features, a lot of value.

FOR:
Nearly everything. Optional extras well worth having are the Data Export Facility for using CFB data in one's own programs; and the Systems Analyser software for running one's own theories.

AGAINST:
Bit like Hitler's liebensraum - demanding more and more living space. The DOS Staking Calculator would be a welcome addition to the Windows version.

VERDICT:
A Rolls-Royce of a program. For the pro and rich amateur who must have the mostest form.

COMPUTER RACEFORM v3

Price: £390 for a full season; prices fall as season progresses

Raceform Ltd, Compton, Newbury, Berkshire RG16 0NL.
Phone: 01635 578080. Fax: 01635 578101.

Company profile:
One of the main horseracing publishing companies. Long history of prestigious weekly newspaper and periodical publishing: titles include Raceform Update, Raceform, Chaseform, Horses In Training and Chaseform and Raceform annuals. Computer Raceform launched in 1992.

Technical details:
PCs 386 or better, at least 4Mb RAM. Each season uses about 6Mb of disk space. Minimum hard disk of 80Mb recommended. Windows.

Software Type:

Full horseracing database, including details on each horse, Raceform Notebook comments written by on-course race-readers, database/system analyzer, ratings, own ratings, statistics etc.

Overview:

Slow start with computers but swift progress after teething trouble. Many features include a List Manager that lets one build lists of horses, jockeys, trainers, sires etc to follow and highlights them automatically.

Ease of Use: ★★★★

Straightforward.

Documentation: ★★★★

Written:

Full manual.

On Screen:

Plenty of guidance.

Technical support:

Full support during office hours. Visits by customers and potential customers welcomed. Demonstrations organised by office staff and agents.

Visual: ★★★

Colour (mono will also work but detracts from versatility).

Range and versatility: ★★★★

Excellent. Comprehensive information on horses, trainers etc.

Value For Money:

A lot of money, a lot of features, a lot of value.

FOR:

Race comments by the company's renowned race-readers. Four ratings per race including Raceform Speed, based on the illustrious Split Second. Own ratings facility. Pace and consistency considered. Collateral form quickly obtained. Edecs service for daily declarations. Multi-layered formbook.

AGAINST:

Time will tell if early hiccups banished for good. Format takes a little getting used to.

VERDICT:

A Daimler of a program. Late starter that has all but caught up with its main rival, the Computer Formbook. Excellent notes on running by top-notch racereaders give this package considerable edge. New version with many enhancements and new features out in 1996.

COMPUTER TIMEFORM

Price: Varies throughout season and according to subscription (with or without modem facility).

Timeform, Timeform House, Halifax HX1 1XE. Phone: 01422 330330.

Company profile:

Leading publishers of horseracing information since 1948.

Technical details:

PCs. Requires 4Mb RAM and up to 50Mb hard disk. Windows 3.1 or newer and preferably 486 processor. For modem 14,400 BPS transmission suggested.

Software Type:

Complete formbook and race ratings/race card service with option of decs/entries by modem.

Overview:

Information from Timeform Perspective, Timeform Race Cards and Timeform Handicap Ledger in one powerful program.

Ease of Use: ★★★

Fairly easy passage through layer upon layer of information.

Documentation: ★★★

Written:

Full manual. Good demonstration version includes tutorials.

On Screen:

No.

Technical support:

Office hours Monday to Friday.

Visual: ★★★

User-defined Windows colours.

Range and versatility: ★★★★

Extensive.

Value For Money:

Very good.

FOR:

Three already well established aids put into computer form.

AGAINST:

Just a little confusing at first with its build-up of so much information. What kept this pioneer off computers so long? Has a little catching up to do on the other two formbook programs.

VERDICT:

A Mercedes to run. I'm Bullish (with apologies to organisation founder, Phil Bull) about this one. Superlative race comments, good ratings.

FORMALYSER v1.1

Price:£38.95

Cheques to D C Beech, KCT, 19 St Johns Avenue, Oulton, Stone, Staffordshire ST15 8UD. Phone: 01785 818377.

Company profile:

Small software writing and training company.

Technical details:

IBM compatible PCs using DOS 3.1 or higher. Runs from hard or floppy disk.

Software Type:

Rates horses with latest information from the Racing Post for the Flat and National Hunt.

Overview:

One of the stand-alones' top weights for data input.

Ease of Use: ★★

Too much shuffling between Racing Post pages. Some 44 inputs per horse most time consuming.

Documentation: ★★★

Written:

Manual.

On Screen:

None needed.

Technical support:

By phone. Internet and Compuserve downloading planned.

Visual: ★★

Colour and black and white.

Range and versatility: ★★★

Average.

Value For Money: ★★★

Lots of analysis at a reasonable price.

FOR:

Good effort to cover lots of ground, especially for jockeys and trainers.

AGAINST:

Badly needs speeding up with data disks or by modem. Difficult to go back to make corrections.

VERDICT:

For those with plenty of time who want a meaty program. Could come good.

HORSE-SENSE v3

Price: £9.95

Chris Mostyn Associates, P O Box 379, Preston, Lancs PR1 9BZ.
Phone: 01772 745193.

Company profile:

Established 1989, writing specialist statistical packages. Started as a part-time business but expanding all the time.

Technical details:

CGA/VGA monitor required. Version 2.1 available at £5 for CGA. Free update discounts if original disk returned with sae.

Software Type:

Winner-finding for Flat and National Hunt.

Overview:

Advises tackling Class races of five to ten runners, all with current exposed form. Racing Post needed for Postmark and Topspeed ratings. Simple, easy to learn program with limited features, thorough in what it does. The cheapest program (excluding Shareware) on the market.

Ease of Use: 

Input minimal. Has cut out the excessive and irritating verification procedure of earlier versions.

Documentation: 

Written:
Can be printed from the disk.

On Screen:
Adequate.

Technical support:

Telephone help 8am to 9pm.

Visual: 

Colour.

Range and versatility: 

Limited.

Value For Money: 

Despite limitations, excellent value as a winner-finder for such a little money.

FOR:

Good value-for-money thinking where the horse with the top Chance of Winning percentage jibs with its lower-than-others rating. Cheapest program of its kind.

AGAINST:

Lack of features. Course and Going omitted. Use of Postmark and Forecast Odds may unbalance own form ratings and overate favourites.

VERDICT:

An easy to learn, reasonably accurate program for the computer/racing novice at a knock-out price.

MICROFORM PLUS

Price: £30

MicroForm Software, 62 Cissbury Road, Tottenham, London N15 5QA.

Company profile:

Small part-time business run by Information Technology professionals. Formula provided by racing professional and developed over five years.

Technical details:

PCs 286 or higher, DOS 3.1 or later, 1Mb hard disk space, 543k RAM. Will not run from floppy disk.

Software Type:

Winner-finding for the Flat.

Overview:

Packing much power, MicroForm Plus could be MegaForm Plus. Has a high strike-rate in certain types of race.

Ease of Use: 

With all the printed and on-screen guidance there is little chance of getting bogged down. Speedy.

Documentation: 

Written:

Fully comprehensive manual with step by step examples.

On Screen:

Context sensitive help from anywhere within the program including references to User Guide page numbers.

Technical support:

None officially given because none is really needed. However, any problems or points personally attended to on the basis of wanting to provide customer care, not as a consumer right.

Visual: ★★

Colour and mono.

Range and versatility: ★★★

Useful options include a Results Manager that tidies records, and the Betting Account Balance.

Value For Money: ★★★

Plenty of punch for small outlay.

FOR:

Powerful predictions in Listed races for 3-y-os and over. Help at hand all along the way.

AGAINST:

Course/Distance and apprentice allowances ignored in the calculations. 'True odds' not shown, preventing comparison with forecast odds when looking for value for money.

VERDICT:

A likeable, well-tested program at the right price.

ORACLE RACING SYSTEM

Price: £75

ESP Software, P O Box 557, Southend-on-Sea, Essex SS0 7JH.
Phone: 01702 434600. Fax: 01702 434888.

Company profile:

In specialist sports software and production since 1989. Oracle in personal use since 1991 and on sale to the public since October 1993. ESP accepted as a member of The Guild of Master Craftsmen .

Technical details:

PCs with minimum 640k RAM and one floppy disk drive. Disks 3.5 inch unless 5.25 requested. Windows version imminent. Runs on any Amiga and Atari ST with 1Mb RAM and a floppy drive.

Software Type:

Winner-finding Flat and National Hunt. A list of horses, updated monthly, who are expected to win on their next outing. Monthly updates at a rate between £40 and £25, on which any new versions of the programs are included.

Overview:

Good but irritating program with excellent forecasting ability. A little commonsense may obviate, for quite a while, the need for updates regarding jockeys, trainers and the combination of the two.

Ease of Use: ★★

Lots of inputs, lots of time. An input error can shut the program down! Confusing layout for some percentages.

Documentation: ★★★★

Written:

Fully descriptive 44-page manual in A5 sized slip case and binder; also a guide to results for at least the previous 12 months.

On Screen:

Adequate guidance.

Technical support:

By telephone 9.30 to 5.30 Monday to Friday.

Visual: ★★

Colour. Not spectacular.

Range and versatility: 

Goes where few others venture with combinations and percentages. Limited options.

Value For Money: 

Price cut from £99.99 makes this even better value than before. The program has a good record for delivering the goods.

FOR:

Potent forecasting factors like successful Jockey/Trainer combinations (shown on-screen) and a variety of percentages such as for type of race, season and distance.

AGAINST:

Monthly list of tips unnecessary and gimmicky.

VERDICT:

Good at its job: predicting winners. Could lead the field one day.

PROFIT MANAGER PLUS v2.0

Price: £149

First Post Racing Ltd, Units 6-7 Venture Park, Corporation Road, Newport, Gwent NP9 06E. Phone: 0800 833015 (Freephone) or 01633 840400.

Company profile:

Established in 1992.

Technical details:

PCs with DOS 3.1 or higher and a floppy drive; and the Amiga A 500 (with PC emulator board). Special PC emulators enables Selection Manager to run on Macintoshes and Ataris.

Software Type:

Two selection programs, Selection Manager 1.2 and First Rate 1.1 and a five-bank Profit Manager.

Overview:

Profit Manager developed over six years. Two run-of-the mill selection methods. Security tokens issued with the software allows only for transfer to hard disk and a back-up.

Ease of Use: Profit Manager: ★★★
Ease of Use: Selection programs: ★★

Any one bank or all five banks of Profit Manager are easily handled. The selection systems are fussy and time-consuming with check-back for virtually every entry.

Documentation:

Written:

Ring-clip manual. Some background theorising confusing and unnecessary.

On Screen:

Satisfactory.

Technical support:

Hardware packages include free four-hour training session (hardly needed) at several UK training centres. Freephone help available.

Visual: ★★

Colour. Nothing spectacular.

Range and versatility: ★★★

Average compared to newer programs. Profit Manager can cut losses.

Value For Money:

Profit Manager raises star value to three.

FOR:

Profit Manager cuts losses.

AGAINST:

Depending on how results fall, Profit Manager can also cut winnings. Fussy inputting for selections. No value for money factor displayed.

VERDICT:

Looks overpriced now against other packages and since price increased from when program reviewed in ODDS ON in November 1993.

PRO-PUNTER 2 Plus

Price: £99 for DOS version
£99 for Pro-Punter Gold (Windows) version.

DGA Software, 437 Kings Road, Ashton-under-Lyne, Lancs OL6 9AT.
Phone: 0161 330 0184.

Company profile:

Full-time business, established in 1987. Other software covers football and golf.

Technical details:

Pro-Punter 2 Plus runs on PCs, DOS, minimum 512k, EGA/VgA/SVGA graphics, ideally hard disk; Atari ST floppy only; and Amiga, floppy and hard disk.

Pro-Punter Gold runs on Windows 3.1 on machines with at least 4Mb RAM.

Software Type:

Winner-finding for Flat and National Hunt. Updates at various discount prices.

Overview:

An expert system that took three years to develop, offering full race analysis/ratings/odds/investment advice. Needs a racing daily for input, which is greatly speeded up using weekly update disks from independent companies. Windows version slicker but DOS version better value for some. A Rapid Race Rater for PCs, the Atari ST and Amstrad PCW costs £25. An efficient Stakemaster is also sold separately.

Ease of Use:
With weekly disks:

Four main and three optional data entry screens accessed from a main central menu look daunting and data entry may take half an hour per race. However, two separate independent organisations supply weekly data update disks for PCs which greatly speed up operations.

They are:

Kingsdown Racing, *phone 01920 830278, £5 per file/week, with discounts;*

Dataform, *phone 0171 638 1138, £40/four weeks.*

A modem service is also on offer with both.

Documentation:

Written:

Fine 44-page user guide.

On Screen:

DOS - no help screens needed. Windows adequate.

Technical support:

9am to 5.30pm Monday to Saturday. Quarterly newsletter, Pro-Punter User (£12 a year), has interesting findings and advice.

Visual: ★★★

Colour and mono. No spectacular graphics.

Range and versatility: ★★★

Excellent options.

Value For Money: ★★★★

An information topweight that gives more winners than most.

FOR:

Comprehensive input. Course option allows inclusion of foreign courses (will configure to metric weights). Identifies value for money horses. Good race selector. Packs in plenty.

AGAINST:

Slow. Add-on options negate the original purpose of the program to be an effective stand-alone. 'No-Bet' advice frustrating after long input sessions (but the inclusion of the race selector in this version cuts down wasted time).

VERDICT:

Good results from selected races. Almost on a par with the big computer form books for options but at a much cheaper rate. One of the best winner-finders on the market.

PUNTER'S PAL v5

Price: £20

R W Lyne, 46 The Avenue, Harrogate, North Yorks HG1 4QD.
Phone: 01423 886415.

Company profile:

The company was the first to put out a try- before-you-buy racing program, Punter's Pal v1, through Shareware in 1988. The program has been updated and improved steadily over the years.

Technical details:

Runs in any PC under DOS.

Software Type:

Rates every horse in a race based upon past form with relevance to the current race.

Overview:

Drop down menus and on-screen input fields make data entry quick and easy. Data can be amended at any time and the factors can be adjusted to develop one's own system.

Ease of Use: ★★★

Fast and easy.

Documentation: ★★★

Written:

17-page manual.

On Screen:

Shareware version has on-disk manual.

Technical support:

Full support for registered users. Non-registered users can try the Shareware version - but no technical support is given until the registration fee of £20 is paid to the author.

Visual: ★★

Colour and mono. Easy to see screens and menus.

Range and versatility: ★★

Limited options. Weighting of factors can be adjusted and saved, then restored and revised to optimise success rate. Uses the Racing Post or Sporting Life.

Value For Money: ★★★

Good value considering the price.

FOR:

Inexpensive. Allows ratings adjustment for maximum advantage.

AGAINST:

Input little more than scrutinising last three races to find class factor.

VERDICT:

Not too much to pay for a program that aims to pick outsiders. May do well with handicaps.

RACEXRAY

Price: £36 or free with 12 month subscription to Smartsig magazine.

P O Box 29, Mansfield NG19 8UA. Phone: 01623 812400.

Company profile:

Self-employed computer consultant, programmer and racing enthusiast. Sales through recommendations. Concerned with statistics and systematic approach to betting.

Technical details:

PCs with DOS 2 or later (machines from 1986). Upmarket equipment (hard disks, printer etc) unnecessary. The program will run from the floppy disk, including the older 5.25 DD disk.

Software Type:

Race-rating system for Flat or National Hunt. The program was developed for use on top class Listed and Group races, although it may be used for any level of competition.

Overview:

Somewhat different from other programs but resembles (as a super model) the Racing Post's Teledata feature. Novel sales ploy to throw in the interesting systems+ magazine edited and produced by the author.

Ease of Use: ★★★★

One of the most user-friendly programs around, for both beginners and experts. It allows race details to be saved to disk.

Documentation: ★★★

Written:

A 16-page A5 size illustrated manual.

On Screen:

Adequate.

Technical support:

Lifetime telephone support.

Visual: ★★

Colour or mono.

Range and versatility:

Limited to prediction essentials.

Value For Money:

Even better value than before now the price has been cut and a 12-month free subscription to the systems magazine has been included.

FOR:

The clear indication of horses running into form, maintaining form or falling back. The charting of key factors for easy viewing.

AGAINST:

Could benefit from the inclusion of options such as a betting manager. Novices may find it lacks a little bite in not plumping firmly for its top XRated.

VERDICT:

A sort of super-Teledata. One for the pros, though the novices should also benefit.

RACINGSYSTEMBUILDER

Price: £99 Starter edition; **£199** Standard; **£299** Professional.

Racedata, Upper Buckenhill Farmhouse, Fownhope, Hereford HR1 4PU.
Phone/Fax 01432 860864.

Company profile:

Racedata is the brainchild of Bill Wilkinson and Tim Drakeford, programmers with an interest in computer modelling. They have run a computer formbook on their own account since 1986. They have written a huge quantity of software which relates to this formbook. RSB, launched in 1995, is their first offering on a user-friendly basis. Tim Drakeford is a former Methodmaker of Raceform Update.

Technical details:

Any standard 386 or 486 or Pentium PC with Windows 3.1 or later. 20, 40 and 44 Mb respectively of hard disk space needed for the three editions, but more recommended, especially if running any kind of disk doubler.

Software Type:

Does not rate individual races but extensively and relatively quickly checks many systems and ideas for systems over years. A National Hunt version likely.

Overview:

Does not analyse and rate individual races. With more than 90 variables and several categories of these it can eliminate the need to pore over years of formbooks by coming up with answers in minutes. The statistics are drawn from a coded database. Annual updates of race statistics planned. A boon to those unfamiliar with running their own huge database.

Ease of Use: ★★★★

Considering the magnitude of information stored and called upon, it is extremely user-friendly.

Documentation: ★★

Written:

Has been kept to a minimum (printed sheets) deliberately.

On Screen:

Comprehensive online context sensitive help.

Technical support:

By phone and fax.

Visual: ★★

Nothing spectacular.

Range and versatility:

Wide-ranging in what it sets out to do: gallops down the years at near breakneck speed.

Value For Money: ★★★★★

One of the best offerings in a decade.

FOR:

A wonderfully systematic attempt to help check on systems and to produce one's own to show a profit. Addictive fun.

AGAINST:

Lack of a class factor based on prizemoney won/wins. Speed and draw factors also missing.

VERDICT:

A dream coming true for the systemites.

SOLIDUS FASTWARE

Price: £439 SF2 (with weekly updates throughout year)
£74 SF1 (no updates but has previous year's form + current year's to date).

Stanza, P O BOX 59, Ipswich IP4 2BL. Phone: Helpline: 0860 157772.

Company profile:

Author Davey Towey qualified groundsman with years of stable experience. BA in Science & Technology. Put prestigious Solidus racing book on market in 1993.

Technical details:

IBM compatible PC 286 or higher, 640K and 45Mb hard disk space to take two season's results (space can be saved by omitting a year's results). DOS 4.1 or later.

Software Type:

DOS only rating system for Flat or National Hunt.

Overview:

Emphasis on speed rating, with distance, class and weight other factors.

Ease of Use: ★★★

Fairly simple menu. SF1 package involves meticulous attention to files and database maintenance.

Documentation: 

Written:

Printed 12-page A5 size booklet. Easier for punter if loading instructions on inside back cover could be transferred to first page.

On Screen:

Adequate.

Technical support:

Telephone support.

Visual: ★★

Colour or mono.

Range and versatility: ★★

Limited to prediction essentials.

Value For Money: 

SF2 package pricey when compared with the comprehensive formbook programs selling at similar prices. SF1 package good value for the DIY inputters.

FOR:

Outstanding speed ratings as to be expected with a scientist who literally has experience at ground level. Author's study and practical knowledge of individual course, going and distance factors put to excellent use.

AGAINST:

Considering the SF2 price, lacking in general features such as a betting manager or comparison of 'true' and forecast odds.

VERDICT:

One of the best speed programs.

THE PUNTER'S REVENGE vII

Price: £39.99 (£5 discount for ODDS ON readers). Most credit card orders accepted.

Route One Developments, Unit 11, Oakfield Avenue, Hitchen, Hertfordshire SG4 9JB. Fax hotline: 01462 435481.

Company profile:

Fairly recently-established software development company.

Technical details:

PCs 286/386/486, 1Mb RAM, 20Mb hard disk, CGA/EGA/VGA/SVGA. Earlier version (£19.95) also runs on Amigas and the Atari ST.

Software Type:

Complete guide to horseracing, including race evaluations and a bets calculator. For the Flat and National Hunt.

Overview:

Vengeance could be at hand. A lot under the bonnet in an easy to operate program.

Ease of Use: 

Instructions are few and easy to follow, using any daily newspaper. Evaluation and analysis are swift.

Documentation: 

Written:

An instruction sheet. Disk and literature well protected in a plastic case.

On Screen:

Full help system.

Technical support:

Not usually required but any queries are dealt with as soon as possible, usually by return of post.

Visual: ★★★

Colour and mono.

Range and versatility: 

Easy race evaluation. Each-way bets can be calculated, with suggested bets from evaluated races. An easy to understand bank account. Weighting can be viewed and altered to suit conditions.

Value For Money: 

At the right price. The earlier version, though lacking some of the Version II refinements, is a bargain at £19.95.

FOR:

Takes the Travel factor into the reckoning. Weighting can be altered. Has picked some big race winners.

AGAINST:

Weighting may need to be amended pretty often. Not an abundance of extras.

VERDICT:

Power to the punter! A good, workmanlike program that has picked many big race winners.

THE SWORD

Price: £129.95

Elswick Enterprises, 17 Greenacres Avenue, Kirkham, Preston PR4 2TX.
Phone: 01253 698843.

Company profile:

Allan Knight, the author, a racing aficionado for years. Produces software and books on the subject. The Sword began jousting in 1995.

Technical details:

Programmed in both DOS and Windows. DOS version will run in 640K standard PC memory and will run on other computers that use a PC emulator.

Software Type:
Covers both Flat and National Hunt.

Overview:
Won a limited computer software challenge competition where only four others finished the 25 Saturdays course. Recommends limiting races for analysis to ten to 12 runners. Needs input from a sporting daily.

Ease of Use: ★★★
Claims to rate each runner in 60 to 90 seconds. A 'secret rule' hacks down the number of races to rate. Mouse-happy entry can have opposite effect of intention to speed total input.

Documentation: ★★★
Written:
A 24-page booklet of instructions and sound betting advice.
On Screen:
Full help system.

Technical support:
Technical advice available from the programmer. General advice on getting the best from the program is dealt with by Allan Knight.

Visual: ★★★
Colour and mono.

Range and versatility: ★★★★
Plenty of useful features includes race selector Merlin, the Fortress staking plan, bar graph and betting guide.

Value For Money: ★★★★
Packs plenty.

FOR:
Early bugs eliminated. Good early successes. Useful facilities.

AGAINST:
Mousemanic Windows version.

VERDICT:
A comparative newcomer to challenge older programs for supremacy.

THE SHIELD

Price: £89.95 for either Flat or NH version.

Address and phone number as for The Sword.

Company profile:
See the Sword.

Is from the same stable as The Sword, but concentrates on handicap races. Good overall success claimed despite warning of losing runs of seven and eight. New out of the stalls and due to deadlines no test has been done on this program at time of going to press.

THE WINNER'S ENCLOSURE

Price: £29.95

DiscOver, PO Box 244, Doncaster DN2 6QZ.

Company profile:

Small publishing and software company. Established in 1991. Trading in Europe, Asia, Australia and New Zealand.

Technical details:

PCs, DOS. Can be run from one floppy disk.

Software Type:

Rates for Win and Place in Flat and National Hunt races. Uses Artificial Intelligence, which should help to improve accuracy in the long term. User-friendly. Requires no previous knowledge of horseracing or computing. Long-standing special offer includes greyhound and soccer programs in the price above (but check before buying). Two-thirds discount given to all users upgrading to a later version.

Overview:

Seemingly basic use of Artificial Intelligence. Nevertheless a promising approach in a field that has enabled computers to trounce Grand Masters in Chess. Results must be fed back to enhance future performance. Much improved professional version promised.

Ease of Use: ★★★★

Very easy, very fast.

Documentation:

Written:

Four-page booklet gives full, easy to understand instructions. Special offer software may be supplied with instructions in the form of an electronic book.

On Screen:

Adequate.

Technical support:

Seldom needed. A software engineer will give a telephone 'talk through' to anyone having difficulty installing or using the program. Individually tailored Batch and PIF files can be written if required. All support is free.

Visual:

Colour and mono.

Range and versatility: ★★

Limited options.

Value For Money: ★★★

Racing and computer novices may like this, also those in a hurry.

FOR:

Its speed and the special offer of extra programs.

AGAINST:

Races limited to ten runners. Looks lightweight. Strike-rate may be lower than claimed though it does turn up winners. No built-in button for a printout.

VERDICT:

Innovative. With the extra programs thrown in it offers much. Some doubt whether such a basic gambit can match the performance of the Artificial Intelligence Chess programs, but a first step nevertheless.

TIPSTER 4 WINDOWS

Price: £34.95

Sidmouth Software, P O Box 7, Sidmouth, Devon EX10 0TD.
Phone: 01404 814547. EMail: Sidsoft@Cpages.Co.Uk

Company profile:

Trading since 1989 and specialising in mail order gambling software, including two pools programs and one for the dogs.

Technical details:

PCs. Input can be taken from a daily newspapers. The Daily Mirror and The Sun recommended.

Software Type:

Selects the best each-way horse at Flat and National hunt meetings.

Overview:

This Windows version is derived from Sidmouth Softwares' Tipster International and Tipster Professional (same prices but provision made to run on Amigas and Ataris, too). The company claim theirs is probably the best-selling racing software on the market.

Ease of Use: 

Inputting, into three grids, is easy but time-consuming - much data goes in after much looking up if using a sporting daily (where strike-rate percentages for top trainers and top jockeys are covered in more depth). Sample races in the database may be called up to get the punter started.

Documentation: 

Written:
12-16 page manual.

On Screen:
Error messages and help files.

Technical support:
A 365-day, 24-hour service. Problems addressed within 48 hours and software modifications are free on receipt of a SAE. A newsletter. Sidsoft News (£9.95 for 12 copies), gives hints and tips from customers and informs on winning runs.

Visual: ★★★
Colour.

Range and versatility: ★★★
Gives the essentials.

Value For Money: ★★★★
Excellent.

FOR:
Good winner-finding ability. This, allied to Sidmouth's mini doubling-up scheme (a mini Martingale), is claimed to produce 'an incredible 92 per cent chance of beating the bookie', based on statistics from 3,000 races over four years.

AGAINST:
Doubling up may end in disaster (though there is undoubted winner-finding potential to make the claims seem plausible). Not too many options.

VERDICT:
Thrills without frills. A goodie. Open the box and double your money?

TIPSTER PLACEPOT 4 WINDOWS v95.1

Price: £44.95

Address and phone number as for Tipster 4 Windows

Company profile:
See Tipster 4 Windows

Technical details:
PCs. Data can be taken from a daily newspapers. The Daily Mirror and The Sun recommended.

Software Type:
Used for the Tote (six selections). Can be used for any multiple bet.

Overview:
An answer to the Placepot fanatic's prayer. The format is derived from

Sidmouth Softwares' Tipster International and Tipster Professional.

Ease of Use: ★★★

Sample races in the database may be called up to get the punter started. Pull-down menus make inputting easy. A little too much use of the mouse when the TAB or ENTER keys would be quicker to jump from box to box.

Documentation: ★★★

Written:

12-page ring-bound manual contains lots of useful advice. A demonstration data sheet comes with the package. Free disk label for backup copy.

On Screen:

Text files.

Technical support:

A 365-day, 24-hour free service.

Visual: ★★★

Colour.

Range and versatility: ★★★

Gives the essentials.

Value For Money: ★★★★

Excellent value. Reputed to have won over a betting shop manager!

FOR:

A Placepot program pioneer. Meets a long-felt need. Selections can also be used in multiple bets. Claims it is designed to move into profit after 20 meetings.

AGAINST:

Very little.

VERDICT:

Makes a good job of being the first program concentrating specifically on the Placepot.

TREVIEW

Price: £150

The Racing Exchange, 28 Anglers Way, Cambridge CB4 1TZ.
Phone: 01223 420909.

Company profile:

Small software house established in 1991.

Technical details:

PCs, 386 model or later. Windows, DOS 3.3 or later, Needs approximately 2Mb hard disk space (data is highly compressed).

Software Type:

Available as two separate systems, for the Flat and National Hunt. Updates £10 per month.

Overview:

Comprehensive data on trainer/jockey statistics. Limited features but thorough in what it does. The system is based on the Sporting Life Trainers Review books. The information comes from the same source and compilers.

Ease of Use:

User-friendly. Statistics on every trainer who had a runner and for every course over the previous five seasons. The data is broken down into every type of race (12 on the Flat, eight over the Jumps) and further broken down by month, by favourite, first time out and jockeys riding. Favourites also analysed by Course.

Documentation:

Written:

Extensive 100-page manual with clear instructions.

On Screen:

Online help.

Technical support:

None officially given, because none is really needed. However any problems or points are personally attended to, although this is strictly on the basis of wanting to provide customer care, not as a consumer right.

Visual:

Colour and mono (ability to change default colour scheme).

Range and versatility:

Strictly limited, though thorough in what it provides.

Value For Money:

The benchmark in its field.

FOR:

Unique in-depth analysis of a very important aspect of horserace forecasting. Excellent filter for other systems.

AGAINST:

No options. Treview sometimes falters in big races, where the punter cannot be helped because no trainer predominates.

VERDICT:

Let the trainer take the strain. Treview is simply the most authoritative source in its field. One for the specialist and the more serious punter.

THE TUTORIAL

Price: £29

Life Unlimited, Eagle Lodge, Longridge, Berwick-upon-Tweed TD15 2XQ.
Phone/Fax: 01289 302467.

Additional programs at £10 each include the New Alpha (how to use Artificial Intelligence to induce rules from data); the Alpha-NH and the Alpha-Flat (£15 for both); the Fleet (uses Baysian Probabilities); the C-Factor (uses Impact Values); the Personal Betting Strategy £15), The Portfolio of four systems derived from the RacingSystemsBuilder (£25) with a betting plan (£20).

Company profile:

Small part-time business, long established. Produces 'electronic' interactive books in connection with gambling software. This is based on original research using Artificial Intelligence, Baysian Probability and Impact Values.

Technical details:

PCs, with DOS. Can run from 3.5 or 5.25 inch floppies. Print-outs available for other users.

Software Type:

Unique, as it is based on modules added to the original Tutorial, which also 'teaches' users to produce their own software and electronic books. Also stand-alone programs applicable to all types of gambling, but principally horseracing.

Overview:

Original approach to successful punting. A multiplicity of programs from an enthusiastic author.

Ease of Use: ★★★★★

Easy inputs, user-friendly, fast - some programs entail only two to three inputs per race.

Documentation: ★★

Written:

None. Prints can be produced from within the software.

On Screen:

Instructions via the user-friendly IRIS interface. Most programs come with their own tutorials, giving the background research.

Technical support:

Available by letter, phone or fax. Quarterly newsletters (£10 each or £35 for the year) give back-up information.

Visual: ★★★

Colour and mono.

Range and versatility:

Considerable, covering forecasting, staking and programming the futuristic way.

Value For Money: 

Deep thought has gone into producing deep programs on the cheap.

FOR:

Originality, ease of use, speed.

AGAINST:

Some programs have not lived up to early promise. Although print-outs can be made from the programs, such original work deserves to arrive with printed instructions.

VERDICT:

Back to the future. While with generally lucrative potential, the programs also give the thinking person the practical ability to go it alone.

A share of the action

The following are among a variety of Shareware products that may be bought for about £2 to £3. Fuller versions are available, often with printed manual, at around £12 to £30, for those satisfied with the original taster.

Shareware may be bought direct from manufacturers or from PC users groups, disk libraries or friends. Some Shareware is also available from electronic bulletin boards.

Much racing Shareware (Freeware) is American, calling for data on such as Pace which is not available in the UK.

However, most of these American programs have enough going for them to make reasonable testing possible and, with a little ingenuity, profitable.

HS40 (five programs, one disk) & TURF ACCOUNTANT v1.1

Price: £3 per disk plus p&p

Shareware Marketing, 3a Queen Street, Seaton, Devon EX12 2NY
Phone: 01297 24088

The best of this American nap hand is ***Doodah v4.3****. It is based on the work of eminent researcher William L Quirin, who analysed more than 80,000 races by computer. Doodah has flexible weighting factors.*

Best Bet *is basic, with no frills: the author claims a 40 per cent win rate for the five-star selections.*

The Cambridge Handicapper v4.1*, like Best Bet, tackles Class, Speed and Going. A pocket calculator would be handy here.*

The Turbo Harness Race Handicapping System v1.3 *relies heavily on Speed, Going and the Draw.*

Blood Lines Rater *gives a numerical rating for more than 1,000 sires but is a very poor relation to Bred Fast-Track (reviewed in the main section).*

Collectively and against other Shareware the Value For Money rating is ★.

JQL HORSE FORM LITE

Price: £2.49 with £14.95 to register.

Springsoft PC Shareware, Springfield House, Llanfynydd, Wrexham, Clwyd LL11 5HW. Phone: 01352 770049

An excellent British program, runs from Windows, so needs a PC with hard disk. It is quick and easy to use and can find good winners. As Shareware it rates ★ ★ ★ ★ for value.

***The Punters Pack**, from the same supplier, costs £7.99 and comes on two disks. Horses, dogs and the pools are covered. There is also a turf accounting program.* ★★

***The Punter's Pal** rates 'less obvious' horses and tries to equate Class and Going with performance. The full version costs a further £19.99. Its Shareware rating is* ★★★

DFL Software, of 13 Holly Road, Northampton, NN1 4QL (phone 01604 24744), who deal exclusively in gambling software, also sell *Doodah, Best Bet, Cambridge Handicapper* and *Turf Accountant*. Prices may vary slightly.

Winners' Enclosure

Now that program pros and cons have been aired, a recap summary of salient features may be useful.

Ton-up tipsters (who have successfully tipped 100-1 shots):

Brimardon Form Plus, The Tipster and **Pro-Punter.**

Programs giving the quickest analysis:

Combayes, The Tutorial and **The Winner's Enclosure.**

Betting manager programs:

Betting Manager and **Profit Manager.**
The former excels in calculating multiple bets in a flash; the latter moderates losses and winnings, depending on how the results fall. Betting Manager should appeal to the punter staking low but trying for a big win.

Several other programs incorporate staking managers, notably **Pro-Punter** and **The Sword**.

Multiple programs:

Boxform Toolkit, Profit Manager Plus, The Sword and **The Tutorial** as well as some Shareware.

Systems analysers:

Computer Form Book, Computer Raceform and **RacingSystemBuilder.**

Do It Yourself programs:

RacingSystemBuilder.

Specialist programs:

Bred Fast-Track for forecasting based on breeding and **Treview,** for trainer/jockey trends. **Formalyser** and **Oracle** also take trainer/jockey trends into its reckoning but in a limited way. **Tipster Placepot 4 Windows** concentrates on that speciality bet while **RacingSystemBuilder** checks/evolves systems.

Most innovative:

Artus, the quirky French entrant that goes for the big one; **RacingSystemBuilder** is the first commercial package wrapped up for novice as well as the computer buff; **The Tutorial** - you have heard of one-horse towns, well, in here can be found a one-horse program, yes, just one horse to check!

Most promising newcomers:

Solidus Fastware, The Sword, The Shield, RacingSystemBuilder and **Tipster Placepot 4 Windows.**

Most ambitious entry:

RacingSystem Builder, which spans the years of data in minutes.

And finally

Best Value For Money:

Compunter, Computer Form Book, Brimardon Formula Plus and **RacingSystemBuilder.**

While there is no guarantee that years of unbroken success behind **Compunter** and **Brimardon Formula Plus** will continue, they have to be judged on what they have achieved over many years.

The Computer Form Book (like Computer Raceform) is the lazy punter's luxury.

Because they have not been on the market quite so long, **Pro-Punter** and **Tipster 4 Windows** programs only just miss the top accolade. **RacingSystemBuilder** is so far unique besides being most effective.

Scratched? Or gone to stud?

Where are they now, programs that ran so well once but which have not been heard of for a long time? They are mentioned here because copies or variants lurk in old computers and in secondhand markets.

The oldest of the lost ones, **Formbase**, appeared at the end of 1988. It was developed from the stable's promising **Racebase** (not to be confused with another author's later program of that name, alas also vanished and itself one of this chapter's missing programs).

The first Racebase as well as its progeny set new standards in forecasting and its influence can be seen in many other programs today.

It still has adherents, one of whom claims to get as good results from it as from the two or three later programs he regularly uses. It does not need updating and so theoretically can carry on galloping, unseen by most, till joined by those Four Horses of the Apocalypse.

Formbase was a quantum leap forward in race forecasting. It was an effective missing link between the cheapest and the most expensive programs. Even against today's entries it would rate a healthy ★★★★ as do the other lost programs listed here. Serious independent efforts are being made to revive the program now that the author is reported to be living abroad.

Neddybank, definitely put down, spoilt its users for choice of features. It was ahead of its time, hitting the market just as the recession began to bite. Expensive to run, it needed daily updates via a modem - there was no alternative such as a weekly disk offered by rivals.

Perhaps a far-seeing outfit will one day give the gifted donkey the kiss of life. One of the program's Australian connections recently contacted me about another matter.

The other **Racebase** specialised in the form of two-year-olds and how this worked out when the animals matured into colts and fillies. It hit some stunning winning streaks.

The Speculator blazed a glory trail in mid-1993, turning up a good ratio of winners. The program should not be confused with another of the same name, brought out earlier by Raymark.

Shortly before the program went over the horizon WinData were getting hyper-hyper over improvements.

Form-Master entered the stalls about the same time as Formbase, in 1988. It found plenty of winners, especially in non-handicaps, but it was time-consuming. The travel aspect of the program had to be updated as stables came and went. But this can easily be accomplished by the assiduous punter today from information in sporting publications.

Classified advertisements inquiring about copies of Form-Master keep appearing in computer magazines. I hear rumblings from one said to have been closely involved in the program that there is a possibility it may reappear.

Have some of the authors of these lost treasures now found the Philosopher's Stone and are they quietly amassing fortunes from the development of their programs?

Weighing in

In this chapter the thinking behind the programs listed and views about the future are expressed by some of the programmers.

Steve Marriott of **Sidmouth Software** writes: 'There is no doubt that by using a computer (and nearly all racing software packages) you can beat the bookies. In every review of *The Tipster* we have returned a profit from a £1 stake invested on the nose of each top rated horse.

'We sell £35,000 gambling software a year including seven per cent overseas. This market seems to have no ceiling and part of our success must be attributed to magazines and papers such as ODDS ON who are willing to spare space for what in some people's eyes is a con.'

Tim Drakeford, of **Racedata**, the *RacingSystemBuilder* company, says: 'The great problem for punters in following any public selection method, whether tipster or computer generated, is that the betting market guarantees negative feedback: the more successful the selections, the more punters follow them, so the shorter the price.

'What made a profit once will cease to do so. RSB allows the individual to tailor his own unique selection methods, avoiding this pitfall'.

Padraig Kirby, founder of the **Gambling Software Users Group**, writes: 'When I was a licensed bookmaker (and an accountant) back in 1967 I made a stunning discovery about the arithmetic of horseracing and I have spent large parts of the years that followed incorporating that discovery into *Compunter*.

'My discovery was a real breakthrough in forecasting the result of a horse race and is easily demonstrated with ranking and chi-squared tests.

'I would stress the word 'breakthrough'. More discoveries are needed.

'The notion that a programmer can sit down and write a good racing program simply by the use of data collection and manipulation is almost certainly mistaken. The profoundest of racing knowledge and racing judgement is also a minimum requirement.'

David Atherton of **DGA Software** and the brain behind the *Pro-Punter* program, says: 'We've been experimenting with a 'learning module' that will enable the software to smarten up its act by reference to past successes - a low-level Artificial Intelligence.

'One of the drawbacks of most programs is the necessity of typing in data from your newspaper. Again, this information is available on-line on subscription, but is expensive.

'So what we need is to develop a system using an optical reader to turn your racing pages into a program-readable file. Only then will we be using the computer's potential, because the drudgery will have finally been eliminated.'

Martin Thompson, of **Brimardon**, says: 'There are several key areas where computer analysis of form has a big advantage over conventional methods.

1. Form data can be quantified and so the problem of winner selection can be tackled mathematically. Computers do such tasks much better than the human brain.

Ratings can be calculated based on aspects of form. Every horse in the race is evaluated in relation to every other, so it is obvious not only which is best, but also how superior it is.

2. The ratings make it much easier to find the horses that represent value for money.

3. Computers are not subject to irrational decisions due to human emotions. Negative factors will be considered, but as a computer works logically and not emotionally, it merely alters a horse's rating downwards - it does not eliminate the horse altogether.

4. Finally, the punter will be more selective in choosing races. This alone will turn many a losing punter into a winner.'

John Mitchell, from **DiscOver**, *The Winner's Enclosure* stable, says: 'While humans can perform many tasks simultaneously - walking, talking and admiring the scenery at the same time, for instance - present computing power limitations restrict practical applications of Artificial Intelligence to one specific subject at a time.

'This does mean, however, that the core algorithm (list of instructions) can be written in a choice of languages and standard computer hardware can be used.

'As computing power increases and programming techniques develop, we can expect to see software capable of concurrent problem solving. This will mean tremendous advances in all sciences. At that point we will have to decide whether AI really is 'artificial'.'

Robin Lloyd writes: 'What of the future? Long established programs like *Brimardon, Compunter, Pro-Punter* and *The Tipster*, and several later starters, have shown the potential for successful computer forecasting. In this, Artificial Intelligence is likely to play an increasing role.

'No wonder the number of compupunters is growing like a snowball gathering momentum and mass that one day may bury the bookie as we know him today (see Tim Drakeford's comments above)!

'What will happen in this eventuality is anybody's guess, for the bookie, of course, is only the middle man taking a percentage of punters' money: punters are backing their choices against other punters.

'If we all win who will pay out?

'It's now microchips with nearly everything - and not least with racing. The computer will continue to change our lives. Including the way we wager.

'And those who have computers now are part of that process.'

Everything you ever wanted to know about horseracing - via your modem

A few years ago, when I used to write brochures and adverts for some of the world's biggest computer companies, people would rapidly become bored if I started talking about my work.

They didn't understand the importance of the RS232 interface, MS-DOS or UNIX, or how significant it was that the HPIB had been used as the basis for ASCII. The only time they seemed to pay attention was when I related the exploits of the German computer pioneer Professor Wanker who worked (it's true!) for the electronics giant Siemens.

Now, however, the tables are turned. You've acquired a computer (or are about to) and the complexities of the technology that almost certainly used to bore you are now something you are probably keen to understand.

I'm afraid I can't help you get to grips with your 864-page User Manual or explain how to recover that vital document which you somehow blimped out by hitting the wrong key. But I can tell you how to enter the extraordinary world of the Internet.

The Internet is the name given to the communications linkage that now exists between tens of thousands of main-frame computers and millions of PC's worldwide. It is an immense repository of knowledge that can be tapped into by anyone who owns a personal computer and a modem.

Until recently the Internet held little interest for followers of horseracing. But now there are dozens of Internet 'sites' that you can call up and download valuable information about the sport.

If you need to find out the parentage of a horse you can activate your communications software, call up an Internet site and access the first four generations of its pedigree in seconds.

If you want to hear news about racing in other countries you can call up sites that are dedicated to providing detailed up-to-date reports about the sport of kings in Australia, Japan, Hong Kong, South Africa and the United States.

If you'd like to read magazines and newspapers dedicated to horseracing you don't have to visit the newsagent. You can call up several publications online and read their latest articles long before you would normally be able to.

I would estimate that the number of Internet sites dedicated to horseracing doubles every three months or so. Therefore I feel confident in predicting that this remarkable phenomenan will soon become the prime source of information for many racing fans. In fact, I would go further. I'd bet good money that in five years' time every single racing publication in the world will have an Internet site and that more punters will obtain their racing information 'online' than from their newsagent.

The great thing about the Internet is that most of the information you get from it is free, and that even when you call up a site in Korea or Japan you only pay for the cost of a local call. Your only major cost will be the monthly bill from the company that links you up to the Internet.

How to get online:

At present, there are over 50 providers in the UK, offering everything from full Internet access down to e-mail and BBS (Bulletin Board Service) only. Prices vary considerably, with some places charging a set amount and then offering unlimted online time, and some charging extra for extra online time.

Probably the top few are:

Demon (phone 0181 371 1234 for info pack or email sales@demon.net)

Compuserve (phone 0800 289458 or email 70006.101@compuserve)

Delphi (phone 0171 757 7080 or email ukservice@delphi.com)

EasyNet (phone 0171 209 0990 or email admin@easynet.co.uk)

Internet UK (phone 01827 713967 or email sales@zipmail.co.uk)

Some useful worldwide web addresses:

These are the most interesting Internet sites I have visited which cover horseracing.

To contact them, all you have to do is enter the relevant Internet address shown below into your communications software and your computer will do the rest.

There are many other horseracing sites on the 'Net' and others are coming online all the time. The best way to keep tabs on them is to call up the *Hay Net* site which is listed here under America.

Australia

AusRace Homepage: Doug Robb

http://www.psy.uwa.edu.au/user/doug/aus/ausrace.html

News on Australian racing plus access to several other Australian racing sites.

Britain

RaceCall

http://www.ws.pipex.com/tis/racing/race.html

Reviews of big races, ante-post odds, racing pictures.

The Way Ahead

http://www.wayahead.com/contents.html

An ambtious and innovative new UK racing magazine that promises to be rather like an online Weekender or Raceform Update minus the results and entries.

Hoof Intro

http://www.cityscape.co.uk/users/gx34/hfintro.html

National Hunt ratings service from software supplier.

France

Minitel

La page des Sports

http://indy2.imt-mrs.fr/webetud/lefaux/homepage.html

Sports news from France.

Hong Kong

The Hong Kong Racing Journal - Home Page

http://www.hk.linkage.net/~journal/

Sophisticated coverage of racing at Sha Tin and Happy Valley.

Ireland

Today's Racing Results

http://server1.internet-eireann.ie/i-events/racing/

Latest results from Ireland and Britain.

Japan

Takechi's Home Page *(as Horse Racing World in Japan)*

http://www.st.rim.or.jp/~takechi/

News and results of horseracing in Japan. The English is a bit weird in places but it's good stuff.

South Africa

SA Thoroughbreds

http://www.aztec.co.za/exinet/horses/index.html

Facts about South African racing plus useful contact addresses.

United States

The Running Horse
http://www.webcom.com/~alauck/index.html
Interesting American site with links to many others.

And they're off...!
http://www.bdt.com/santa_anita/welcome.html
Santa Anita racecourse news.

Las Vegas Horse/Sportsbook Project
http://geisel.nevada.edu/~manray/books.html
Author/racing fan maintains an interesting array of articles about US racing.

Pedgree Query
http://owl.frontier.com/pedigree/
An online database that contains the four-generation pedigrees of over 100,000 horses. It has a bias towards American-bred runners but it still covers about 80 per cent of the horses who contest European Group and Listed races. It not only gives their pedigrees, it also provides their Dosage Indexes.

American Turf Monthly
http://www.webcom.com/~alauck/atm.html
America's best-selling horseracing magazine. The articles generally offer betting advice and systems of a fairly high order, though with an understandable American bias.

Daily Racing Form
http://www.itsdata.com
Online racing form from the American equivalent of the Sporting Life. (You need to download software and pay a £55 start up fee to use the site fully.)

The Hay Net
http://digmo.org/~kpautz/haynet/racing.html
A good starting point for exploring the horseracing information available on the Internet. The Hay Net lists just about every horseracing site on the Internet. Just click on any of the sites listed and your computer will jump there in minutes.

Thoroughbred Times
http://www.iglou.com/tbred/
The world's best-selling thoroughbred breeding magazine.

Equibase
http://www.thoroughbred.org/equibase/
News on American racing including official runners, likely odds and results.

Betting on the Internet

Wagernet

http://www.vegas.com/wagernet/waghome.html

Bet against other Internet users on a wide variety of racing and sporting events.

Betpoint

You need to buy Betpoint's software to access their private site but it's only £19.99. At the site you get the latest prices and results, and can bet on many future sporting events as well as today's racing. Bets are paid for by Switch or Delta or Credit Account with Betpoint.

Contact Betpoint, PO Box 537, London SW8 1DJ or call 0800 581 066 for details.

Guardian Gambling

http://www.guardian.co.uk/guardian/gambling

Have a punt at the interactive Guardian gambling web-site.

Intertops

http://www.intertops.co.at/inter/engl Germany's biggest bookie takes bets online on sports events and the lottery but not on horseraces.

The above article is by NICK MORDIN and is reproduced by kind permission of ODDS ON magazine where it first appeared (December 1995).